THE
YAGE
LETTERS

William Burroughs
&
Allen Ginsberg

CITY LIGHTS BOOKS

Library of Congress Catalog Card Number : 63-12222

© 1963 by William S. Burroughs & Allen Ginsberg

Third Printing November 1966

The cover photo of a *curandero* from the Vaupes region of Colombia is reprinted by permission of the Botanical Museum of Harvard University. The authors' thanks must be given to Aileen Lee and Alan Ansen who in 1953 helped type and preserve Burroughs' letters and to Melville Hardiment who later preserved Ginsberg's. The 1953 letters were subsequently published in BIG TABLE and KULCHUR. Burroughs' 1960 letter was in FLOATING BEAR No. 5. ' I Am Dying, Meester? ' was in CITY LIGHTS JOURNAL No. 1. Ginsberg's 1960 letter and his note ' To Whom It May Concern ' have not been printed before. Drawings by Ginsberg were included in his letter from Pucallpa.

CITY LIGHTS BOOKS are published at the City Lights Bookstore, Columbus & Broadway, San Francisco 11, California, New York distributors: Bookazine, 43 East 10th Street, New York, N. Y. Overseas distributors: Mandarin Books Ltd., 22 Notting Hill Gate, London, W.11, England. Printed in U.S.A.

CONTENTS

IN SEARCH OF YAGE (1953)

January 15, 1953
Hotel Colon, Panama

Dear Allen,

I stopped off here to have my piles out. Wouldn't do to go back among the Indians with piles I figured.

Bill Gains was in town and he has burned down the Republic of Panama from Las Palmas to David on paregoric. Before Gains, Panama was a p.g. town. You could buy four ounces in any drug store. Now the druggists are balky and the Chamber of Deputies was about to pass a special Gains Law when he threw in the towel and went back to Mexico. I was getting off junk and he kept nagging me why was I kidding myself once a junkie always a junkie. If I quit junk I would become a sloppy lush or go crazy taking cocaine.

One night I got lushed and bought some paregoric and he kept saying over and over, ' I *knew* you'd come home with paregoric. I *knew* it. You'll be a junkie all the rest of your life ' and looking at me with his little cat smile. Junk is a cause with him.

I checked into the hospital junk sick and spent four days there. They would only give me three shots of morphine and I couldn't sleep from pain and heat and deprivation besides which there was a Panamanian hernia case in the same room with me and his friends came and stayed all day and half the night — one of them did in fact stay until midnight.

Recall walking by some American women in the corridor who looked like officers' wives. One of them was saying, ' I don't know why but I just can't eat sweets.'

' You got diabetes lady,' I said. They all whirled around and gave me an outraged stare.

After checking out of the hospital, I stopped off at the U.S. Embassy. In front of the Embassy is a vacant lot with weeds and trees where boys undress to swim in the polluted waters of the bay-home of a small venomous sea snake. Smell of excrement and sea water and young male lust. No letters. I stopped again to buy two ounces of paregoric. Same old Panama. Whores and pimps and hustlers.

' Want nice girl? '

' Naked lady dance? '

' See me fuck my sister? '

No wonder food prices are high. They can't keep them down on the farm. They all want to come in the big city and be pimps.

I had a magazine article with me describing a joint outside Panama City called the Blue Goose. ' This is anything goes joint. Dope peddlers lurk in the men's room with a hypo loaded and ready to go. Sometimes they dart out of a toilet and stick it in your arm without waiting for consent. Homosexuals run riot.'

The Blue Goose looks like a Prohibition era road house. A long one story building run down and covered with vines. I could hear frogs croaking from the woods and swamps around it. Outside a few parked cars, inside a dim bluish light. I remembered a prohibition era road house of my adolescence and the taste of gin rickeys in a mid west summer. (Oh my God! And the August moon in a violet sky and Billy Bradshinkel's cock. How sloppy can you get?)

Immediately two old whores sat down at my table without being asked and ordered drinks. The bill for one round was $6.90. The only thing lurking in the men's room was an insolent demanding lavatory attendant. I may add that far from running riot in Panama I never scored for one boy there. I wonder what a Panamanian boy would be like. Probably cut. When they say anything goes they are referring to the joint not the customers.

I ran into my old friend Jones the cab driver, and bought

some C off him that was cut to hell and back. I nearly suffocated myself trying to sniff enough of this crap to get a lift. That's Panama. Wouldn't surprise me if they cut the whores with sponge rubber.

The Panamanians are about the crummiest people in the Hemisphere — I understand the Venezuelans offer competition — but I have never encountered any group of citizens that brings me down like the Canal Zone Civil Service. You can not contact a civil servant on the level of intuition and empathy. He just does not have a receiving set, and he gives out like a dead battery. There must be a special low frequency civil service brain wave.

The Service men don't seem young. They have no enthusiasm and no conversation. In fact they shun the company of civilians. The only element in Panama I contact are the hip spades and they are all on the hustle.

Love,
Bill

P.S. Billy Bradshinkel got to be such a nuisance I finally had to kill him :

The first time was in my model A after the Spring prom. Billy with his pants down to his ankles and his tuxedo shirt still on, and jissom all over the car seat. Later I was holding his arm while he vomited in the car headlights, looking young and petulant with his blond hair mussed standing there in the warm Spring wind. Then we got back in the car and turned the lights off and I said, ' Let's again.'

And he said, ' No we shouldn't.'

And I said, ' Why not? ' and by then he was excited too so we did it again, and I ran my hands over his back under his tuxedo shirt and held him against me and felt the long baby hairs of his smooth cheek against mine and he went to sleep there and it was getting light when we drove home.

After that in the car several times and one time his family was away and we took off all our clothes and afterwards I watched him sleeping like a baby with his mouth a little open.

That Summer Billy caught typhoid and I went to see him every day and his mother gave me lemonade and once his father gave me a bottle of beer and a cigarette. When Billy was better we used to drive out to Creve Coeur Lake and rent a boat and go fishing and lie on the bottom of the boat with our arms around each other's shoulders not doing anything. One Saturday we explored an old quarry and found a cave and took our pants off in the musty darkness.

I remember the last time I saw Billy was in October of that year. One of those sparkling blue days you get in the Ozarks in Autumn. We had driven out into the country to hunt squirrels with my .22 single shot, and walked through the autumn woods without seeing anything to shoot at and Billy was silent and sullen and we sat on a log and Billy looked at his shoes and finally told me he couldn't see me again (notice I am sparing you the falling leaves).

' But why Billy? Why? '

' Well if you don't know I can't explain it to you. Let's go back to the car.'

We drove back in silence and when we came to his house he opened the door and got out. He looked at me for a second as if he was going to say something then turned abruptly and walked up the flagstone path to his house. I sat there for a minute looking at the closed door. Then I drove home feeling numb. When the car was stopped in the garage I put my head down on the wheel sobbing and rubbing my cheek against the steel spokes. Finally Mother called to me from an upstairs window was anything wrong and why didn't I come in the house. So I wiped the tears off my face and went in and said I was sick and went upstairs to bed. Mother brought me a bowl of milk toast on a tray but I couldn't eat any and cried all night.

After that I called Billy several times on the phone but he always hung up when he heard my voice. And I wrote him a long letter which he never answered.

Three months later when I read in the paper he had been killed in a car wreck and Mother said, ' Oh that's the Bradshinkel boy. You used to be such good friends didn't you? '

I said, ' Yes Mother ' not feeling anything at all.

And I got a silo full of queer corn where that come from. Another routine : A man who manufactures memories to order. Any kind you want and he guarantees you'll believe they happened just that way — (As a matter of fact I have just about sold myself Billy Bradshinkel). A line from the Japanese Sandman provides themesong of story, ' Just an old second hand man trading new dreams for old.' Ah what the Hell ! Give it to Truman Capote.

Another bit of reminiscence but genuine. Every Sunday at lunch my grandmother would disinter her dead brother killed 50 years ago when he dragged his shotgun through a fence and blew his lungs out.

' I always remember my brother such a lovely boy. I hate to see boys with guns.'

So every Sunday at lunch there was the boy lying by the wood fence and blood on the frozen red Georgia clay seeping into the winter stubble.

And poor old Mrs. Collins waiting for the cataracts to ripen so they can operate on her eye. Oh God ! Sunday lunch in Cincinati !

January 25, 1953
Hotel Mulvo Regis, Bogota

Dear Al,

Bogota is on a high plain surrounded by mountains. The grass of the savannah is bright green, and here and there black stone Pre-columbian monoliths are set up in the grass. A gloomy sombre looking town. My hotel room is a windowless cubicle (windows are a luxury in South America) with green composition board walls and the bed too short.

For a long time I sat there on the bed paralyzed with bum kicks. Then I walked out into the thin cold air to get a drink, thanking God I didn't hit this town junk sick. I had a few drinks and went back to the hotel where an ugly queer waiter served me indifferent meal.

Next day I went to the University to get information on Yage. All sciences are lumped in The Institute. This is a red brick building, dusty corridors, unlabeled offices mostly locked. I climbed over crates and stuffed animals and botanical presses. These articles are continually being moved from one room to another for no discernible reason. People rush out of offices and claim some object from the litter in the hall and have it carried back into their offices. The porters sit around on crates smoking and greeting everybody as ' Doctor '.

In a vast dusty room full of plant specimens and the smell of formaldehyde, I saw a man looking for something he could not find with an air of refined annoyance. He caught my eye.

' Now what have they done with my cocoa specimens? It was a new species of wild cocoa. And what is this stuffed condor doing here on my table? '

The man had a thin refined face, steel rimmed glasses, tweed coat and dark flannel trousers. Boston and Harvard unmistakeably. He introduced himself as Doctor Schindler. He was connected with a U.S. Agricultural Commission.

I asked about Yage. ' Oh yes,' he said, ' We have specimens here. Come along and I'll show you,' he said taking one last look for his cocoa. He showed me a dried specimen of the Yage vine which looked to be a very undistinguished sort of plant. Yes he had taken it. ' I got colors but no visions.'

He told me exactly what I would need for the trip, where to go and who to contact. I asked him about the telepathy angle. ' That's all imagination of course,' he said. He suggested the Putomayo as being the most readily accessible area where I could find Yage.

I took a few days to assemble my gear and dig the capitol. For a jungle trip you need medicines; snake bite serum, penicillin, enterovioformo and aralen are essentials. A hammock, a blanket and a rubber bag known as a tula to carry your gear in.

Bogota is high and cold and wet, a damp chill that gets inside you like the inner cold of junk sickness. There is no heat anywhere and you are never warm. In Bogota more than any other city I have seen in Latin America you feel the dead weight of Spain sombre and oppressive. Everything official bears the label Made in Spain.

As ever,
William

January 30
Hotel Niza, Pasto

Dear Al,

I took a bus to Cali because the autoferro was booked solid for days. Several times the cops shook down the bus and everybody on it. I had a gun in my luggage stashed under the medicines but they only searched my person at these stops. Obviously anyone carrying guns would bypass the

stops or pack his guns where these sloppy laws wouldn't
search. All they accomplish with the present system is to
annoy the citizens. I never met anyone in Colombia who has
a good word for the Policia Nacional.

The Policia Nacional is the Palace Guard of the Conservative Party (the army contains a good percentage of
Liberals and is not fully trusted). This (the P.N.) is the most
unanimously hideous body of young men I ever laid eyes
on, my dear. They look like the end result of atomic radiation.
There are thousands of these strange loutish young men in
Colombia and I only saw one I would consider eligible and
he looked ill at ease in his office.

If there is anything to say for the Conservatives I didn't
hear it. They are an unpopular minority of ugly looking shits.

The road led over mountain passes down into the curious
middle region of Tolima on the edge of the war zone. Trees
and plains and rivers and more and more Policia Nacional.
The population contains some of the best looking and the
ugliest people I ever saw. Most of them seemed to have
nothing better to do than stare at the bus and the passengers
and especially at the gringo. They would stare at me until
I smiled or waved, then smile back the predatory toothless
smile that greets the American all through South America.

' Hello Mister, One cigarette? '

In a hot dusty coffee stop town I saw a boy with delicate
copper features, beautiful soft mouth and teeth far apart in
bright red gums. Fine black hair fell in front of his face.
His whole person exuded a sweet masculine innocence.

At one custom stop I met a nacional law who had fought
in Korea. He pulled open his shirt to show me the scars on
his unappetizing person.

' I like you guys,' he said.

I never feel flattered by this promiscuous liking for

Americans. It is insulting to individual dignity, and no good ever comes from these America lovers.

In the late afternoon I bought a bottle of brandy and got drunk with the bus driver. Stopped over in Armenia and went on to Cali next day with the autoferro.

Vegetation semitropical with bamboo and bananas and papayas, Cali is a relatively pleasant town with a nice climate. You do not feel tension here. Cali has a high rate of straight no political crime. Even safe crackers. (Big operators in the crime are rare in South America).

I met some old time American residents who said the country was in a hell of a shape.

' They hate the sight of a foreigner down here. You know why? It's all this Point four and good nabor crap and financial aid. If you give these people anything they think " oh so he needs me ". And the more you give the bastards the nastier they get.'

I heard this line from old timers all over S.A. It does not occur to them that something more basic is involved here than the activities of Point four. Like the U.S. Pegler fans say, ' The trouble is Unions.' They would still say it spitting blood from radiation sickness. Or in process of turning into crustaceans.

On to Popayan by autoferro. This is a quiet university town. Some one told me the place was full of intellectuals but I did not see any. A curious, negativistic hostility pervades the place. Walking in the main square a man bumped into me with no apology, his face blank, catatonic.

I was drinking coffee in a cafe where a young man with an archaic Jewish-Assyrian face approached me and went into a long spiel about how much he liked foreigners and how he wanted to buy me a drink or at least pay for my coffee. As he talked it became obvious that he did not like foreigners and had no intention of buying me a drink. I paid for my coffee and left.

In another cafe some gambling game like bingo was in progress. A man came in emitting curious yelps of imbecile hostility. Nobody looked up from their bingo.

In front of the post office were Conservative posters. One of them read : ' Farmers the army is fighting for your welfare. Crime degrades a man and he can't live with himself. Work elevates him towards God. Cooperate with the police and the military. *They only need your information.*' (Italics mine).

It's your duty to turn in the guerillas and work and know your place and listen to the priest. What an old con! Like trying to sell the Brooklyn Bridge. Not many people are buying it. The majority of Colombians are Liberals.

The Policia Nacional slouch on every corner, awkward and self-conscious, waiting to shoot somebody or do anything but stand there under hostile eyes. They have a huge gray wagon that rides around and around the town with no prisoners in it.

I walked out along a dusty road. Rolling country with green grass, cattle and sheep and small farms. A horribly diseased cow was standing in the road covered with dust. A roadside shrine with a glass front. The ghastly pinks and blues and yellows of religious art.

Saw a movie short about a priest in Bogota, runs a brick factory and makes homes for the workers. The short shows the priest fondling the bricks and patting the workers on the back and generally putting down the old Catholic con. A thin man with distraught neurotic eyes. Finally he gave a speech to the effect : Wherever you find social progress or good works or anything good there you will find the church.

His speech had nothing to do with what he was really saying. There was no mistaking the neurotic hostility in his eyes, the fear and hate of life. He sat there in his black uniform nakedly revealed as the advocate of death. A business man without the motivation of avarice, cancerous activity sterile and blighting. Fanaticism without fire or energy exuding a musty odor of spiritual decay. He looked sick and dirty — though I guess he was clean enough actually — with a suggestion of yellow teeth, unwashed underwear and psychosomatic liver trouble. I wonder what his sex life could be.

Another short showed a get together of the Conservative party. They all looked congealed, a frozen crust on the country. The audience sat there in complete silence. Not a murmur of approval or dissent. Nothing. Naked propaganda falling flat in dead silence.

Next day took a bus for Pasto. Driving in the place hit me in the stomach with a physical impact of depression and horror. High mountains all around. High thin air. The inhabitants peering out of sod roofed huts, their eyes red with smoke. The hotel was Swiss run and excellent. I walked around the town. Ugly crummy looking populace. The higher you got the uglier the citizens. This is a leprosy area. (Leprosy in Colombia is more prevalent in high mountains, T.B. on the coast). It seemed like every second person had a hairlip or one leg shorter than the other or a blind festering eye.

I went into a cantina and drank aguardiente and played the mountain music on the juke box. There is something archaic in this music strangely familiar, very old and very sad. Decidedly not Spanish in origin, nor is it oriental. Shepherd music played on a bamboo instrument like a pan-pipe, pre-classic, Etruscan perhaps. I have heard similar music in the mountains of Albania where pre-Greek, Ilyrian racial strains linger. A phylogenetic nostalgia conveyed by this music — Atlantean?

I saw working behind the bar what looked at first like an

attractive boy of 14 or so (the place was dimly lit owing to a partial power failure). Going over by the bar for a closer look, I saw his face was old, his body swollen with pith and water like a rotten melon.

An Indian was sitting at the next table fumbling in his pockets, his fingers numb with alcohol. It took him several minutes to pull out some crumbled bills—what my grand-mother, a violent prohibitionist, used to describe as 'dirty money'—he caught my eye and smiled a twisted broken smile. 'What else can I do?'

In one corner a young Indian was pawing a whore, an ugly woman with a bestial ill natured face and the dirty light pink dress of the calling. Finally she disengaged herself and walked out. The young Indian looked after her in silence without anger. She was gone and that was that. He walked over to the drunk and helped him up and together they staggered out with the sad sweet resignation of the mountain Indian.

I had an introduction from Schindler to a German who runs a wine factory in Pasto. I found him in a room full of books warmed by two electric heaters. The first heat I had seen in Colombia. He had a thin ravaged face, sharp nose, downcurving mouth, a junkie mouth. He was very sick. Heart bad, kidneys bad, high blood pressure.

'And I used to be tough as nails,' he said plaintively, 'What I want to do is go to the Mayo Clinic. A doctor here gave me an injection of iodine which upset my whole meta-bolism. If I eat anything with salt my feet swell up like that.'

Yes he knew the Putumayo well. I asked about Yage.

'Yes, I sent some to Berlin. They made tests and reported the effect is identical to the effect of hashish . . . there is a bug in the Putumayo, I forget what they call it, like a big grasshopper, such a powerful aphrodisiac, if it flies on you and you can't get a woman right away you will die. I have seen them running around jacking off from contact with this animal . . I have one in alcohol around some place . . . no, come to think it was lost when I moved here after the war . . . another thing I have been trying to get information on it . . . a vine you chew and all your teeth fall out.'

' Just the thing for practical jokes on your friends,' I said.

The maid brought in tea and pumpernickel and sweet butter on a tray.

' I hate this place but what is a fellow to do? I have my business here. My wife. I'm stuck.'

Will leave here in next few days for Macoa and the Putumayo. Won't write from there since mail service beyond Pasto is extremely unreliable depending on volunteer carrier-bus and truck drivers mostly. More letters are lost than delivered. These people do not have even the concept of responsibility.

As Ever,
Willy Lee

February 28, 1953
Hotel Niza, Pasto

Dear Allen :

On my way back to Bogota with nothing accomplished. I have been conned by medicine men (the most inveterate drunk, liar and loafer in the village is invariably the medicine man), incarcerated by the law, rolled by a local hustler (I thought I was getting that innocent back woods ass, but the kid had been to bed with six American oil men, a Swedish Botanist, a Dutch Ethnographer, a Capuchin father known locally as The Mother Superior, a Bolivian Trotskyite on the lam, and jointly fucked by the Cocoa Commission and Point Four). Finally I was prostrated by malaria. I will relate events more or less chronologically.

I took a bus to Macoa which is the capital of the Putumayo and end of the road. From there on you go by mule or canoe. For some reason these end of road towns are always God awful. Anyone expecting to outfit himself there will find they have nothing he needs in the stores. Not even citronella — and no one in these end of the road towns knows anything about the jungle.

I arrived in Macoa late at night and consumed a ghastly Colombian soft drink under the dubious eyes of a national cop who could not make up his mind whether to question me or not. Finally he got up and left and I went to bed. The night was cool, about like Puyo, another awful end of the road town.

When I woke up next morning I began to get bum kicks still in bed. I looked out the window. Cobble stone, muddy streets, one story buildings mostly shops. Nothing out of the ordinary but in all my experience as a traveler — and I have seen some God awful places — no place ever brought me down like Macoa. And I don't know exactly why.

Macoa has about 2000 inhabitants and sixty national cops. One of them rides around all day through the four streets of the town on a motor bicycle. You can hear him from any place in town. Radios with extra loud speakers in every cantina make a horrible discordant noise (there are no juke boxes in Macoa where you can play what you want to hear). The police have a brass band they bang around three or four times a day starting in the early morning. I never saw any signs of disorder in this town which is well out of the war zone. But there is an air of unresolved and unsoluble tension about Macoa, the agencies of control out in force to put down uprising which does not occur. Macoa is The End Of The Road. A final stalemate with the cop riding around and around on his motor bicycle for all eternity.

I went on to Puerto Limon which is about 30 miles from Macoa. This town can be reached by truck. Here I located an intelligent Indian and ten minutes later I had a Yage vine. But the Indian would not prepare it since this is the monopoly of the Brujo (medicine man).

This old drunken fraud was crooning over a man evidently down with malaria. (Maybe he was chasing the evil spirit out of his patient and into the gringo. Anyway I came down with malaria two weeks to the day later.) The Brujo told me he had to be half lushed up to work his witchcraft and cure people. The high cost of liquor was working a hardship on the sick, he was only hitting two cylinders on a short count of lush. I bought him a pint of aguardiente and he agreed to prepare the Yage for another quart. He did in fact prepare a pint of cold water infusion after misappropriating half the vine so that I did not notice any effect.

That night I had a vivid dream in color of the green jungle and a red sunset I had seen during the afternoon. A composite city familiar to me but I could not quite place it. Part New York, part Mexico City and part Lima which I had not seen at this time. I was standing on a corner by a wide street with cars going by and a vast open park down the street in the distance. I can not say whether these dreams had any connection with Yage. Incidentally you are supposed to see a city when you take Yage.

I spent a day in the jungle with an Indian guide to dig the jungle and collect some Yoka, a vine the Indians use to prevent hunger and fatigue during long trips in the jungle. In fact, some of them use it because they are too lazy to eat.

The Upper Amazon jungle has fewer disagreeable features

than the Mid-West stateside woods in the summer. Sand flies and jungle mosquitoes are the only outstanding pests and you can keep them off with insect repellent. I didn't have any at this time. I never got any ticks or chiggers in the Putumayo. The trees are tremendous, some of them 200 feet tall. Walking under these trees I felt a special silence, a vibrating soundless hum. We waded through clear streams of water (who started this story you can't drink jungle water? Why not?)

Yoka grows on high ground and it took us four hours to get there. The Indian cut a Yoka vine and shaved off a handful of the inner bark with a machete. He soaked the bark in a little cold water, squeezed the water out of the bark and handed me the infusion in a palm leaf cup. It was faintly bitter but not unpleasant. In 10 minutes I felt a tingling in my hands and a nice lift somewhat like benzedrine but not so tight. I walked the four hours back over jungletrail without stopping and could have walked twice that far.

After a week in Puerto Limon I went to Puerto Umbria by truck and down to Puerto Assis by canoe. These canoes are about 30 feet long with an outboard motor. This is standard method of travel on the Putumayo. The motors are out of commission about half the time. This is because people take them apart and leave out the pieces they consider non-essential. Also they economize on grease so the motors burn out.

I arrived in Puerto Assis at 10 p.m. and as soon as I stepped out of the canoe a federal cop wanted to see my papers. There is more check on papers in the quiet zones like Putumayo than in Villvicencio which is edge of the war zone. In the Putumayo you won't be five minutes whistle stop before they check your papers. They expect trouble to come from outside in the form of a foreigner — gods knows why.

Next day the governor, who looked like a degenerate strain of monkey, found an error in my tourist card. The consul in Panama had put down 52 instead of 53 in the date. I tried to explain this was an error, clear enough in view of the dates on my plane tickets, passport, receipts, but the man was bone stupid. I don't think he understands yet. So the cop gave my luggage a shake missing the gun but decided to impound the medicine gun and all. The sanitary inspector put in his two cents suggesting they go through the medicines.

' For God's sake,' I thought, ' Go inspect an outhouse.'

They informed me I was under town arrest pending a decision from Macoa. So I was stuck in Puerto Assis with nothing to do but sit around all day and get drunk every night. I had planned to take a canoe trip up the Rio Quaymes to contact the Kofan Indians who are known Yage artists, but the governor would not let me leave Puerto Assis.

Puerto Assis is a typical Putumayo River town. A mud street along the river, a few shops, one cantina, a mission where Capuchin fathers lead the life of Riley, a hotel called the Putumayo where I was housed.

The hotel was run by a whorish looking landlady. Her husband was a man of about 40, powerful and vigorous, but there was a beat look in his eyes. They had seven daughters and you could tell by looking at him that he would never have a son. At least not by that woman. This giggling brood of daughters kept coming into my room (there was no door, only a thin curtain) to watch me dress and shave and brush my teeth. It was a bum kick. And I was the victim of idiotic pilfering — a catheter tube from my medical kit, a jock strap, vitamin B tablets.

There was a boy in town who had once acted as a guide

to an American naturalist. This boy was the local Mister Specialist. You find one of these pests all over South America. They can say, 'Hello Joe' or 'O.K.' or 'Fucky fucky.' Many of them refuse to speak Spanish thus limiting conversation to sign language.

I was sitting on a worn out inverted canoe that serves as a bench in the main drag of Puerto Assis. The boy came and sat with me and began talking about the Mister who collected animals, 'He collected spiders, and scorpions and snakes.' I was half asleep lulled by this litany when I heard, 'And he was going to take me back to the states with him,' and woke up. Oh God, I thought, that old line.

The boy smiled at me showing gaps in his front teeth. He moved a little closer on the bench. I could feel my stomach tighten.

'I have a good canoe,' he said, 'why don't you let me take you up the Guaymes? I know all the Indians up there.'

He looked like the most inefficient guide in the Upper Amazon but I said, 'Yes.'

That night I saw the boy in front of the cantina. He put his arms around my shoulders and said, 'Come in and have a drink, Mister,' letting his hand slip down my back and off my ass.

We went in and got drunk under the weary wise eyes of the bartender and took a walk out along the jungle trail. We sat down in the moonlight by the side of the trail and he let his elbow fall into my crotch and said, 'Mister,' next thing I heard was, 'How much you gonna give me?'

He wanted $30 evidently figuring he was a rare commodity in the Upper Amazon. I beat him down to $10 bargaining under increasingly disadvantageous conditions. Somehow he managed to roll me for $20 and my underwear shorts (when he told me to take my underwear all the way off I thought, a passionate type, my dear, but it was only a maneuver to steal my skivies).

After five days in Puerto Assis I was well on the way to establish myself as a citizen in the capacity of village wastrel. Meanwhile sepulchral telegrams issued periodically from Macoa. ' The case of the foreigner from Ohio will be resolved.' And finally, ' Let the foreigner from Ohio be returned to Macoa.'

So I went back up the river with the cop (I was technically under arrest). In Puerto Umbria I came down with chills and fever. Arriving in Macoa on a Sunday, the Commandante was not there so the second in command had me locked up in a wood cubicle without even a bucket to piss in. They put all my gear unsearched in with me. A typical South American touch. I could have had a machine gun concealed in my luggage. I took some aralen and lay down shivering under the blanket. The man in the next cell was confined for lack of some document. I never did understand the details of his case. Next morning the Commandante showed up and I was summoned to his office. He shook hands pleasantly, looked at my papers, and listened to my explanation.

' Clearly an error,' he said, ' This man is free.' What a pleasure it is to encounter an intelligent man in such circumstances.

I went back to the hotel and went to bed and called a doctor. He took my temperature and said, ' Carramba ! ' and gave me an injection of quinine and liver extract to offset secondary anemia. I continued the aralen. I had some codeine tablets to control malaria headache so I lay there sleeping most of the time for three days.

I will go to Bogota, have my tourist card reassembled and return here. Travel in Colombia is difficult even with the soundest credentials. I have never seen such ubiquitous and annoying police. You are supposed to register with the police wherever you go. This is unpardonable stupidity. If I was an active Liberal what could I do in Puerto Assis aside from taking the place over at gun point?

As Ever,
William

March 3
Hotel Nueva Regis, Bogota

Dear Al:

Bogota horrible as ever. I had my papers corrected with the aid of U.S. Embassy. Figure to sue the truss off PAA for fucking up the tourist card.

I have attached myself to an expedition — in a somewhat vague capacity to be sure — consisting of Doc Schindler, two Colombian Botanists, two English Broom Rot specialists from the Cocoa Commission, and will return to the Putumayo in convoy. Will write full account of trip when I get back to this town for the third time.

As Ever,
Bill

April 15
Hotel Nuevo Regis, Bogota

Dear Al:

Back in Bogota. I have a crate of Yage. I have taken it and know more or less how it is prepared. By the way you may see my picture in *Exposure*. I met a reporter going in as I was going out. Queer to be sure but about as appetizing as a hamper of dirty laundry. Not even after two months in the brush, my dear. This character is shaking down the South

American continent for free food and transport, and discounts on everything he buys with a ' We-got-like-two-kinds-of-publicity-favorable-and-unfavorable-which - do - you - want,- Jack?' routine. What a shameless mooch. But who am I to talk?

Flashback : Retraced my journey through Cali, Popayan and Pasto to Macoa. I was interested to note that Macoa dragged Schindler and the two Englishmen as much as it did me.

This trip I was treated like visiting royalty under the mis- apprehension I was a representative of the Texas Oil Company travelling incognito. (Free boat rides, free plane rides, free chow; eating in officers' mess, sleeping in the governor's house.)

The Texas Oil Company surveyed the area a few years ago, found no oil and pulled out. But everyone in the Putu- mayo believes the Texas Company will return. Like the second coming of Christ. The governor told me the Texas Company had taken two samples of oil 80 miles apart and it was the same oil, so there was a pool of the stuff 80 miles across under Macoa. I heard this same story in a back water area of East Texas where the oil company made a survey and found no oil and pulled out. Only in Texas the pool was 1000 miles across. The beat town psyche is joined the world over like the oil pool. You take a sample anywhere and it's the same shit. And the governor thinks they are about to build a railroad from Pasto to Macoa, and an airport. As a matter of fact the whole of Putumayo region is on the down grade. The rubber business is shot, the cocoa is eaten up with broom rot, no price on rotenone since the war, land is poor and there is no way to get produce out. The dawdling psychophrenia of small town boosters. Like I should think some day soon boys will start climbing in through the transom and tunneling under the door.

Several times when I was drunk I told some one, ' Look. There is no oil here. That's why Texas pulled out. They won't ever come back. Understand? ' But they couldn't believe it.

We went out to visit a German who owned a finca near Macoa. The British went looking for wild coca with an Indian guide. I asked the German about Yage.

' Sure,' he said, ' My Indians all use it.' A half hour later I had 20 pounds of Yage vine. No trek through virgin jungle and some old white haired character saying, ' I have been expecting you my son.' A nice German 10 minutes from Macoa.

The German also made a date for me to take Yage with the local Brujo (at that time I had no idea how to prepare it.)

The medicine man was around 70 with a baby smooth face. There was a sly gentleness about him like an old time junkie. It was getting dark when I arrived at this dirt floor thatch shack for my Yage appointment. First thing he asked did I have a bottle. I brought a quart of aguardiente out of my knapsack and handed it to him. He took a long drink and passed the bottle to his assistant. I didn't take any as I wanted straight Yage kicks. The Brujo put the bottle beside him and squatted down by a bowl set on a tripod. Behind the bowl was a wood shrine with a picture of the Virgin, a crucifix, a wood idol, feathers and little packages tied with ribbons. The Brujo sat there a long time without moving. He took another long swig on the bottle. The women retired behind a bamboo partition and were not seen again. The Brujo began crooning over the bowl. I caught ' Yage Pintar ' repeated over and over. He shook a little broom over a bowl and made a swishing noise. This is to whisk away evil spirits who might slip in the Yage. He took a drink and wiped his mouth and went on crooning. You can't hurry a Brujo. Finally he uncovered the bowl and dipped about an ounce more or less of black liquid which he handed me in a dirty red plastic cup. The liquid was oily and phosphorescent. I drank it straight down. Bitter foretaste of nausea. I handed the cup back and the medicine man and the assistant took a drink.

I sat there waiting for results and almost immediately had the impulse to say, 'That wasn't enough. I need more.' I have noticed this inexplicable impulse on the two occasions when I got an overdose of junk. Both times before the shot took effect I said, 'This wasn't enough. I need more.'

Roy told me about a man who came out of jail clean and nearly died in Roy's room. 'He took the shot and right away said, "That wasn't enough" and fell on his face out cold. I dragged him out in the hall and called an ambulance. He lived.'

In two minutes a wave of dizziness swept over me and the hut began spinning. It was like going under ether, or when you are very drunk and lie down and the bed spins. Blue flashes passed in front of my eyes. The hut took on an archaic far-Pacific look with Easter Island heads carved in the support posts. The assistant was outside lurking there with the obvious intent to kill me. I was hit by violent, sudden nausea and rushed for the door hitting my shoulder against the door post. I felt the shock but no pain. I could hardly walk. No coordination. My feet were like blocks of wood. I vomited violently leaning against a tree and fell down on the ground in helpless misery. I felt numb as if I was covered with layers of cotton. I kept trying to break out of this numb dizziness. I was saying over and over, 'All I want is out of here.' An uncontrollable mechanical silliness took possession of me.

Hebrephrenic meaningless repetitions. Larval beings passed before my eyes in a blue haze, each one giving an obscene, mocking squawk (I later identified this squawking as the croaking of frogs) — I must have vomited six times. I was on all fours convulsed with spasms of nausea. I could hear retching and groaning as if I was some one else. I was lying by a rock. Hours must have passed. The medicine man was standing over me. I looked at him for a long time before I believed he was really there saying, 'Do you want to come into the house?' I said, 'No,' and he shrugged and went back inside.

My arms and legs began to twitch uncontrollably. I reached for my nembutals with numb wooden fingers. It must have taken me ten minutes to open the bottle and pour out five capsules. Mouth was dry and I chewed the nembutals down somehow. The twitching spasms subsided slowly and I felt a little better and went into the hut. The blue flashes still in front of my eyes. Lay down and covered myself with a blanket. I had a chill like malaria. Suddenly very drowsy. Next morning I was all right except for a feeling of lassitude and a slight back-log nausea. I paid off the Brujo and walked back to town.

We all went down to Puerto Assis that day. Schindler kept complaining the Putumayo had deteriorated since he was there ten years ago. 'I never made a Botanical expedition like this before,' he said. 'All these farms and *people*. You have to walk miles to get to the jungle.'

Schindler had two assistants to carry his luggage, cut down trees and press specimens. One of them was an Indian from the Vaupes region where the method of preparing Yage is different from the Putumayo Kofan method. In Putumayo the Indians cut the vines into 8 inch pieces using about five sections to a person. The pieces of vine are crushed with a rock and boiled with a double handful of leaves from another plant — tentatively identified as ololiqui — the mixture is boiled all day with a small amount of water and reduced to about two ounces of liquid.

In the Vaupes the bark is scraped off about three feet of vine to form a large double handful of shavings. The bark is soaked in a liter of cold water for several hours, and the liquid strained off and taken over a period of an hour. No other plant is added.

I decided to try some Yage prepared Vaupes method. The Indian and I started scraping off bark with machetes (the inner bark is the most active). This is white and sappy at first but almost immediately turns red on exposure to air. The landlady's daughters watched us pointing and giggling. This is strictly against Putumayo protocol for the preparation of Yage. The Brujo of Macoa told me if a woman witnesses the preparation the Yage spoils on the spot and will poison anyone who drinks it or at least drive him insane. The old women-are-dirty-and-under-certain-circumstances-poison-ous routine. I figured this was a chance to test the woman pollution myth once and for all with seven female creatures breathing down my neck, poking sticks in the mixture finger-ing the Yage and giggling.

The cold water infusion is a light red color. That night I drank a quart of infusion over a period of one hour. Except for blue flashes and slight nausea — though not to the point of vomiting — the effect was similar to weed. Vividness of mental imagery, aphrodisiac results, silliness and giggling. In this dosage there was no fear, no hallucinations or loss of control. I figure this dose as about one third the dose that Brujo gave me.

Next day we went on down to Puerto Espina where the governor put us up in his house. That is we slung our hammocks in empty rooms on the top floor. A coolness arose between the Colombians and the British because the Colombians refused to get up for an early start, and the British complained the Cocoa Commission was being sabotaged by a couple of ' lazy spics.'

Every day we plan to get an early start for the jungle. About 11 o'clock the Colombians finish breakfast (the rest of us waiting around since 8) and begin looking for an incompetent guide, preferably someone with a finca near town. About 1 we arrive at the finca and spend another hour eating lunch. Then the Colombians say, ' They tell us the jungle is far. About 3 hours. We don't have time to make it today.' So we start back to town, the Colombians collecting a mess of plants along the way. ' So long as they can collect any old weed they don't give a ruddy fuck,' one of the Englishmen said to me after an expedition to the nearest finca.

There was supposed to be plane service out of Puerto Espina. Schindler and I were ready to go back to Bogota at this point, so there we sit in Puerto Espina waiting on this plane and the agent doesn't have a radio or any way of finding out when the plane gets there if it gets there and he says, ' Sure as shit boys one of these days you'll look up and see the Catalina coming in over the river flashing in the sun like a silver fish.'

So I says to Doc Schindler, ' We could grow old and simple-minded sitting around playing dominoes before any sonofabitching plane sets down here and the river getting higher every day and how to get back up it with every motor in Puerto Espina broke? '

(The citizens who own these motors spend all the time fiddling with their motors and taking the motors apart and leaving out pieces they consider non-essential so the motors never run. The boat owners do have a certain Rube Goldberg ingenuity in patching up the stricken motor for one last more spurt — but this was a question of going up the river. Going down river you will get there eventually motor or no, but coming up river you gotta have some means of propulsion.)

Sure you think it's romantic at first but wait til you sit there five days onna sore ass sleeping in Indian shacks and eating yoka and same hunka nameless meat like the smoked pancreas of a two toed sloth and all night you hear them fiddle fucking with the motor — they got it bolted to the porch — 'buuuuurt spluuuu . . . . ut . . . . spluuuu . . . . ut,' and you can't sleep hearing the motor start and die all night and then it starts to rain. Tomorrow the river will be higher.

So I says to Schindler, ' Doc, I'll float down to the Atlantic before I start back up that fuckin river.'

And he says, ' Bill, I haven't been 15 years in this sonofabitch country and lost all my teeth in the service without picking up a few angles. Now down yonder in Puerto Leguisomo — they got like military planes and I happen to know the commandante is Latah.' (Latah is a condition occuring in South East Asia. Otherwise normal, the Latah cannot help doing whatever anyone tells him to do once his attention has been attracted by touching him or calling his name.)

So Schindler went on down to Puerto Leguisomo while I stayed in Puerto Espina waiting to hitch a ride with the Cocoa Commission. Every day I saw that plane agent and he came on with the same bullshit. He showed me a horrible looking scar on the back of his neck. ' Machete,' he said. No doubt some exasperated citizen who went berserk waiting on one of his planes.

The Colombians and the Cocoa Commission went up the San Miguel and I was alone in Puerto Espina eating in the

Commandante's house. God awful greasy food. Rice and fried platano cakes three times a day. I began slipping the platanos in my pocket and throwing them away later. The Commandante kept telling me how much Schindler liked this food — (Schindler is an old South American hand. He can really put down the bullshit) — did I like it? I would say, ' Magnificent,' my voice cracking. Not enough I have to eat his greasy food. I have to say I like it.

The Commandante knew from Schindler I had written a book on ' marijuana '. From time to time I saw suspicion seep into his dull liverish eyes.

' Marijuana degenerates the nervous system,' he said looking up from a plate of platanos.

I told him he should take Vitamin B1 and he looked at me as if I had advocated the use of a narcotic.

The Governor regarded me with cold disfavor because one of the gasoline drums belonging to the Cocoa Commission had leaked on his porch. I was expecting momentarily to be evicted from the governmental mansion.

The Cocoa Commission and the Colombians came back from the San Miguel in a condition of final estrangement. It seems the Colombians had found a finca and spent three days there lolling about in their pajamas. In the absence of Schindler I was the only buffer between the two factions and suspect by both parties of secretly belonging to the other (I had borrowed a shot gun from one of the Colombians and was riding in the Cocoa Commission boat).

We went on down the river to Puerto Leguisomo where the Commandante put us up in a gun boat anchored in the Putumayo. There were no guns on it actually. I think it was the hospital ship.

The ship was dirty and rusty. The water system did not function and the W.C. was in unspeakable condition. The

Colombians run a mighty loose ship. It wouldn't surprise me to see someone shit on the deck and wipe his ass with the flag. (This derives from dream that came to me in 17th century English. 'The English and French delegates did shit on the floor, and tearing the Treaty of Seville into strips with such merriment did wipe their backsides with it, seeing which the Spanish delegate withdrew from the conference.')

Puerto Leguisomo is named for a soldier who distinguished himself in the Peruvian War in 1940. I asked one of the Colombians about it and he nodded, 'Yes, Leguisomo was a soldier who did something in the war.'

'What did he do?'

'Well, he did *something.*'

The place looks like it was left over from a receding flood. Rusty abandoned machinery scattered here and there. Swamps in the middle of town. Unlighted streets you sink up to your knees in.

There are five whores in town sitting out in front of blue walled cantinas. The young kids of Puerto Leguisomo cluster around the whores with the immobile concentration of tom cats. The whores sit there in the muggy night under one naked electric bulb in the blare of juke box music, waiting.

* Inquiring in the environs of Puerto Leguisomo I found the use of Yage common among both Indians and whites. Most everybody grows it in his backyard.

After a week in Leguisomo I got a plane to Villavencenio, and from there back to Bogota by bus.

So here I am back in Bogota. No money waiting for me (check apparently stolen), I am reduced to the shoddy expedient of stealing my drinking alcohol from the university laboratory placed at disposal of the visiting scientist.

Extracting Yage alcoloids from the vine, a relatively simple process according to directions provided by the Institute. My experiments with extracted Yage have not been conclusive. I do not get blue flashes or any pronounced sharpening of mental imagery. Have noticed aphrodisiac effects. The extract makes me sleepy whereas the fresh vine is a stimulant and in overdose convulsive poison.

Every night I go into a cafe and order a bottle of pepsi-cola and pour in my lab alcohol. The population of Bogota lives in cafes. There are any number of these and always full. Standard dress for Bogota cafe society is a gabardine trench coat and of course suit and tie. A South American's ass may be sticking out of his pants but he will still have a tie.

Bogota is essentially a small town, everybody worrying about his clothes and looking as if he would describe his job as responsible. I was sitting in one of these white collar cafes when a boy in a filthy light gray suit, but still clinging to a frayed tie asked me if I spoke English.

I said, 'Fluently,' and he sat down at the table. A former employee of the Texas Company. Obviously queer, blond, German looking, European manner. We went to several cafes. He pointed people out to me saying, 'He doesn't want to know me any more now that I am without work.'

These people, correctly dressed and careful in manner, did in fact look away and in some cases call for the bill and leave. I don't know how the boy could have looked any less queer in a $200 suit.

One night I was sitting in a Liberal cafe when three civilian Conservative gun men came in yelling 'Viva los Conservadores' hoping to provoke somebody so they could shoot him. There was a middle aged man of the type who features a loud mouth. The others sat back and let him do the yelling. The other two were youngish, ward heelers, corner boys, borderline hoodlums. Narrow shoulders, ferret faces and smooth, tight, red skin, bad teeth. It was almost too pat. The two hoodlums looked a little hang dog and ashamed of themselves like the young man in the limerick who said, ' I'll admit I'm a bit of a shit.'

Everybody paid and walked out leaving the loud mouthed character yelling ' Viva El Partido Conservador ' to an empty house.

As Ever,
Bill

May 5
930 Jose Leal, Lima

Dear Allen :

This finds me in Lima which is enough like Mexico City to make me homesick. Mexico is home to me and I can't go there. Got a letter from my lawyer — I am sentenced in absentia. I feel like a Roman exiled from Rome. Plan to hit Peru jungle for additional Yage material. Will spend a few weeks digging Lima.

Went through Ecuador fast as possible. What an awful place it is. Small country national inferiority complex in most advanced stage.

Ecuadorian Miscellanea : *Esmeraldas* hot and wet as a turkish bath and vultures eating a dead pig in the main drag and everywhere you look there is a Nigra scratching his balls. The inevitable Turk who buys and sells everything. He tried to cheat me on every purchase and I spent an hour arguing with this bastard. The Greek shipping agent with his dirty silk shirt and no shoes and his dirty ship that left Esmeraldas seven hours late.

On the boat I talked to a man who knows the Ecuador jungle like his own prick. It seems jungle traders periodically raid the Auca (a tribe of hostile Indians. Shell lost about twenty employees to the Auca in two years) and carry off women they keep penned up for purposes of sex. Sounds interesting. Maybe I could capture an Auca boy.

I have precise instructions for Auca raiding. It's quite simple. You cover both exits of Auca house and shoot everybody you don't wanna fuck.

Arriving in Manta a shabby man in a sweater started opening my bags. I thought he was a brazen thief and gave him a shove. Turns out he was customs inspector.

The boat gave out with a broken propeller at Las Playas half way between Manta and Guayaquil. I rode ashore on a balsa raft. Arrested on the beach suspect to have floated up from Peru on the Humboldt Current with a young boy and a tooth brush (I travel light, only the essentials) so we are hauled before an old dried up fuck, the withered face of cancerous control. The kid with me don't have paper one. The cops keep saying plaintively :

' But don't you have any papers *at all?* '

I talked us both out in half an hour using the ' We-got-like-two-types-publicity-favorable-and-unfavorable-which-do-you-want? ' routine. I am down as writer on tourist card.

Guayaquil. Every morning a swelling cry goes up from the kids who sell Luckies in the street — ' A ver Luckies,' ' Look here Luckies ' — will they still be saying ' A ver Luckies ' a hundred years from now? Nightmare fear of stasis. Horror of being finally *stuck* in this place. This fear has followed me all over South America. A horrible sick feeling of final desolation.

' La Asia,' a Chinese restaurant in Guayaquil, looks like 1890 whorehouse opium den. Holes eaten by termites in the floor, dirty tasselled pink lamps. A rotting teak-wood balcony.

Ecuador is really on the skids. Let Peru take over and civilize the place so a man can score for the amenities. I never yet lay a boy in Ecuador and you can't buy any form of junk.

As Ever,
W. Lee

P.S.   Met a Pocho cab driver — the Pocho is type found in Mexico who dislikes Mexico and Mexicans. This cab driver told me he was Peruvian but he couldn't stand Peruvians. In Ecuador and Colombia no one will admit anything is wrong with his jerk water country. Like small town citizens in U.S. I recall an army officer in Puerto Leguisomo telling me :

' Ninety percent of the people who come to Colombia never leave.'

He meant, presumably, they were overcome by the charms of the place. I belong to the ten percent who never come back.

As Ever,
Bill

May 12, 1953
Lima

Dear Allen,

I have been looking for what a Waugh character calls ' louche little bistros' with conspicuous success. The bars around the Wholesale Market — Mercado Mayorista — are so full of boys they spill out onto the street, and all wise and available to the yankee dollar — (one) — never saw anything like it since Vienna in '36. The little bastards steal up a breeze though. Lost a watch and 15 dollars already. The watch didn't run. I never had one that did.

Last night I checked into a hotel with a barefooted Indian to the hilarious amusement of the hotel clerk and his friends

(I don't think the average stateside hotel clerk would be amused at such an occurence).

Met a boy and went with him to a dance place. Right in the middle of this well lighted non queer dime and dance joint he put his hand on my cock. So I reciprocated and no one paid it any mind. Then he tried to find something worth stealing in my pocket but I had prudently hidden my money in my hat band. All this routine, you understand, is completely good natured and without a trace of violence overt or potential. Finally we cut out together and took a cab and he embraced me and kissed me yet and went to sleep on my shoulder like an affectionate puppy but insisted on getting out at his place.

Now you must understand this is average *non queer* Peruvian boy, a bit juvenile delinquent to be sure. They are the least character armored people I have ever seen. They shit or piss anywhere they feel like it. They have no inhibitions in expressing affection. They climb all over each other and hold hands. If they do go to bed with another male, and they all will for money, they seem to enjoy it. Homosexuality is simply a human potential as is shown by almost unanimous incidents in prisons — and nothing human is foreign or shocking to a South American. I am speaking of the South American at best, a special race part Indian, part white, part god knows what. He is not, as one is apt to think at first fundamentally an Oriental nor does he belong to the West. He is something special unlike anything else. He has been blocked from expression by the Spanish and the Catholic Church. What we need is a new Bolivar who will really get the job done. This is I think what the Colombian Civil War is basically about — the fundamental split between the South American Potential and the Repressive Spanish life fearing armadillos. I never felt myself so definitely on one side and unable to see any redeeming features in the other. South America is a mixture of strains all necessary to realize the potential form. They need white blood as they know — Myth of White God — and what did they get but the fucking Spaniards. Still they had the advantage of weakness. Never would have gotten the English out of here. They would have created that atrocity known as a White Man's Country.

South America does not force people to be deviants. You can be queer or a drug addict and still maintain position. Especially if you are educated and well mannered. There is deep respect here for education. In the U.S. you have to be a deviant or exist in dreary boredom. Even a man like Oppenheimer is a deviant tolerated for his usefulness. Make no mistake *all* intellectuals are deviants in U.S.

Extensive Chinatown. I think you could score for junk here. In Columbia and Ecuador nobody ever heard of such a thing. A little weed among coast side Negroes. Coca, but only in leaf form, among the Indians.

Incidentally you most always see plenty blood in these louche Peruvian bistros. Ramming broken glass in opponents face is standard practice. Everybody does it here.

Love,
Bill

May 23
Lima

Dear Al,

Enclose a routine I dreamed up.* The idea did come to
me in a dream from which I woke up laughing —

Rolled for $200 in traveller checks. No loss really as
American Express refunds. Recovering from a bout of Pisco
neuritis, and Doc has taken a lung x-ray. First Caqueta
malaria, then Esmeraldas grip, now Pisco neuritis — (Pisco
is local liquor. Seems to be poison) — can't leave Lima until
neuritis clears up.

May 24

Ho hum dept. Rolled again. My glasses and a pocket knife.
Losing all my fucking valuables in the service.

This is a nation of kleptomaniacs. In all my experience as
a homosexual I have never been the victim of such idiotic
pilferings of articles no conceivable use to anyone else. Glasses
and traveller's checks yet.

Trouble is I share with the late Father Flanagan — he of
Boy's Town — the deep conviction that there is no such thing
as a bad boy.

---

* This is Burroughs' first *routine,* ' Roosevelt After Inauguration.' The
form then took on a life of its own, like the talking asshole in
Naked Lunch; subsequent letters to Ginsberg developed much of
the material of that volume. ' Roosevelt After Inauguration ' was
printed in *Floating Bear No. 9*; the editor, poet Leroi Jones, was
arrested for sending this issue through U.S. Government mails;
after a year of harassment Jones was vindicated. Copies of a new
pirated edition of this *routine* are obtainable from City Lights Books
at 50c postpaid.

Got to lay off the juice. Hand shaking so I can hardly write. Must cut short.

Love,
Bill

June 18
Hotel Touriste
Tingo Maria, Peru

Dear Allen :

Comfortable well-run hotel like a mountain resort. Cool climate. Very high jungle. A group of upper class Peruvians in the hotel. Every few minutes one of them yells ' Senor *Pinto* ' — (he runs the hotel) — this is Latin American humorous routine. Like they look at a dog and yell ' Perro ' and everybody laughs.

Talked to a slightly crazed school teacher from California who chewed with her mouth open. The president arrived in Tingo Maria while I was there. Terrible nuisance. No dinner til 9 o'clock and I made a scene with the waiter and walked to town and ate a greasy meal.

Stuck here til tomorrow on bum steer. I was supposed to see a man about Yage and it turns out he moved away five years ago. This is a farming community with Yugoslav and Italian colonists and a U.S. Point Four Experimental Agriculture Station. As dull a crew of people as I ever saw. Farming towns are awful.

This place gives me the stasis horrors. The feel of *location* of being just where I am and nowhere else is unendurable. Suppose I should have to live here?

Did you ever read H. G. Wells' *The Country of the Blind?* About a man stuck in a country where all the other inhabitants had been blind so many generations they had lost the concept of sight. He flips.

'But don't you understand I can *see*?'

As Ever,
Bill

July 8
930 Jose Leal, Lima

Dear Allen :

Back in Lima after three day bus ride. Last five days in Pucallpa I was waiting to leave, but trapped by rain and impassible roads and the plane booked solid.

The Naval Lieutenant did a hideous strip tease with his character armor. Everybody yelling, 'For God's sake keep it on.' He began goosing the waiter and when I passed his room in the morning he would rush to the door and show me a hard on and say, 'Hello Bill.' Even the other Peruvians were embarrassed.

The furniture salesman wanted to go in the cocaine business and get rich and live in Lima and drive a fishtail Cadillac. Oh God. People think all they have to do is go in shady business and they will get rich over night. They don't realize that business shady or legitimate is the same fucking headache. And the old German went on and on about the treasure.

They were driving me crazy with their silly talk and their stupid Spanish jokes. I felt like Ruth amidst the alien corn. When they said that American literature did not exist and English literature was very poor, I lost my temper and told them Spanish literature belonged in the outhouse on a peg with the old Montgomery Ward catalogues. I was shaking with rage and realized how the place was dragging me.

Met a young Dane and took Yage with him. He immediately vomited it up and avoided me after that — he
evidently thought I had tried to poison him and he was
saved only by this prompt reaction of his hygenic Scandina-
vian gut. I never knew a Dane that wasn't bone dull.

Terrible bus trip back to Tingo Maria where I got drunk
and was helped to bed by the cutest assistant truck driver.

Hung up two days in Huanaco. An awful dump. Spent my
time wandering around taking pictures trying to get the bare
dry mountains, the wind in the dusty poplar trees, the little
parks with statues of generals and cupids, and Indians lolling
about with a special South American abandon chewing coca
— the government sells it in controlled shops — and doing
absolutely nothing. At 5 o'clock had a few drinks in a Chinese
restaurant, where the owner picked his teeth and went over
his books. How sane they are and how little they expect from
life. He looked like junk to me but you can never be sure
with the Chinese. They are all basically junkies in outlook.
A lunatic came in the bar and went into a long incompre-
hensible routine. He had the figure $17,000,000 written on
the back of his shirt and turned around to show it to me.
Then he went over and harangued the owner. The owner
sat there picking his teeth. He showed neither contempt nor
amusement nor sympathy. He just sat there picking a molar
and occasionally taking the toothpick out and looking at the
end of it.

Passed through some of the highest towns in the world.
They have a curious exotic Mongolian or Tibetan look.
Horribly cold.

Three times ' all the foreigners ' were asked to get out of
the bus and register with the police : passport number, age,
profession. All this pure formality. No trace of suspicion or

interrogation. What do they do with these records? Use them for toilet paper I expect.

Lima cold damp and depressing. Went to the Mercado. None of the boys around any more. Bum kick to go in a bar I used to like, nobody there I know or want to know, the bar has been moved for no organic reason from one side of the joint to the other — different waiters, nothing I want to hear on the juke box — (am I in the right bar?) — everybody has gone and I am alone in a nowhere place. Every night the people will be uglier and stupider, the fixtures more hideous, the waiters ruder, the music more grating on and on like a speedup movie into a nightmare vortex of mechanical disintegration and meaningless change.

I did see one boy in the Mercado I knew before I left Lima. He looked *years older* (I had been away six weeks). When I first saw him he wouldn't drink, saying with a shy smile :

' I am still a boy.'

Now he was drunk. Scar under left eye. I touched it and said, ' Knife? '

He said, ' Yes ' and smiled, his eyes glazed and bloodshot.

Suddenly I wanted to leave Lima right away. This feeling of urgency has followed me like my ass all over South America. I have to be somewhere at a certain time (in Guayaquil I dragged the Peruvian consul out of his house after office hours so I could get a visa and leave a day earlier).

Where am I going in such a hurry? Appointment in Talara, Tingo Maria, Pucallpa, Panama, Guatemala, Mexico City? I don't know. Suddenly I have to leave right now.

Love,
Bill

*   *

*

SEVEN YEARS LATER (1960)

June 10, 1960
Estafeta Correo
Pucallpa, Peru

Dear Bill,

I'm still in Pucallpa — ran into a little plump fellow, Ramon
P—— who'd been friend to Robert Frank (photographer
of our movie) in '46 or so here. Ramon took me to his
Curandero — in whom he has a lot of faith and about whose
supernatural curing Powers he talks a lot, too much, about
— The Maestro, as he's called, being a very mild and simple
seeming cat of 38 or so — who prepared a drink for 3 of
us the other night; and then last night I attended a regular
Curandero all night drinking session with about 30 other men
and women in a hut in jungly outskirts of Pucallpa behind
the gaswork field.

The first time, much stronger than the drink I had in
Lima, Ayahuasca can be bottled and transported and stay
strong, as long as it does not ferment — needs well closed
bottle. Drank a cup — slightly old stuff, several days old and
slightly fermented also — lay back and after an hour (in
bamboo hut outside his shack, where he cooks) — began seeing
or feeling what I thought was the Great Being, or some sense
of It, approaching my mind like a big wet vagina — lay back
in that for a while — only image I can come up with is of
a big black hole of God-Nose thru which I peered into a
mystery — and the black hole surrounded by all creation —
particularly colored snakes — all real.

I felt somewhat like what this image represents, the sense
of it so real.

The eye is imaginary image, to give life to the picture.
Also a great feeling of pleasantness in my body, no nausea.
Lasted in different phases about 2 hours — the effects wore
off after 3 — the phantasy itself lasted from $\frac{3}{4}$ of hour after

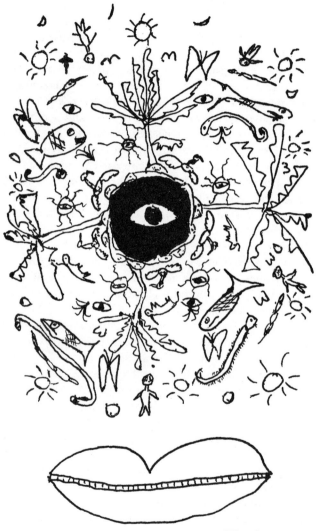

The Great Being

I drank to 2½ hours later more or less.

Went back and talked to The Maestro, gave him 35 soles ($1.50) for services and talked with him about peyote and LSD — he'd heard of peyote — he's a mestizo who studied in San Martin (upper Huallaga territory) — he gave me samples of his mix — uses young cultivated Ayahuasca plant in his back yard, and mixes that about half and half with a catalyst known as the 'Mescla' which is another leaf known in Chama indian language as Cahua (pron Coura) and locally by him in Pucallpa is called Chacruna. Said he'd get me more samples to bring back to Lima Natural History Museum to identify. Cooks the mixes together all day and strains the broth, gives the drained leaves a second cook too. Anyway the preparation is not excessively secret — I think Schultes saw and knows the preparation. Can add other leaves of other plants too, I don't know these combinations to try out — he seemed generally interested in drugs — serious — and not mercenary at all — good type — has quite a following here — does physical cures, his speciality.

Anyway to make long story short, went back to formal group session in huts last night — this time the brew was prepared fresh and presented with full ceremony — he crooning (and blowing cigarette or pipe smoke) tenderly over the cupmouth for several minutes before — (enamel cup, I remember your plastic cup) — then I light cigarette, blow a puff of smoke over cup, and drain. Saw a shooting star — Aerolith — before going in, and full moon, and he served me up first — then lay down expecting God knows what other pleasant vision and then I began to get high — and then the whole fucking Cosmos broke loose around me, I think the strongest and worst I've ever had it nearly — (I still reserve the Harlem experiences, being Natural, in abeyance. The

LSD was Perfection but didn't get me so deep in nor so horribly in) — First I began to realize my worry about the mosquitoes or vomiting was silly as there was the great stake of life and Death — I felt faced by Death, my skull in my beard on pallet on porch rolling back and forth and settling finally as if in reproduction of the last physical move I make before settling into real death — got nauseous, rushed out and began vomiting, all covered with snakes, like a Snake Seraph, colored serpents in aureole all around my body, I felt like a snake vomiting out the universe — or a Jivaro in head-dress with fangs vomiting up in realization of the Murder of the Universe — my death to come — everyone's death to come — all unready — I unready — all around me in the trees the noise of these spectral animals the other drinkers vomiting (normal part of the Cure sesseions) in the night in their awful solitude in the universe — vomiting up their will to live, be preserved in this body, almost — Went back and lay down — Ramon came over quite tender and nurse like (he hadn't drunk, he's sort of an aide to help the sufferers) asked me if I was OK and ' Bien Mareado ' (Good and drunk?) — I said ' Bastante ' and went back to listen to the spectre that was approaching my mind — The whole hut seemed rayed with spectral presences all suffering transfiguration with contact with a single mysterious Thing that was our fate and was sooner or later going to kill us — the Curandero crooning, keeping up a very tender, repeated and then changing simple tune, comfort sort of, God knows what signified — seemed to signify some point of reference I was unable to contact yet — I was frightened and simply lay there with wave after wave of death-fear, fright, rolling over me till I could hardly stand it, didn't want to take refuge in rejecting it as illusion, for it was too real and too familiar — especially as if in rehearsal of Last Minute Death my head rolling back and forth on the

The Vomiter

blanket and finally settling in last position of stillness and
hopeless resignation to God knows what Fate — for my being
— felt completely lost strayed soul — outside of contact with
some Thing that seemed present — finally had a sense that
I might face the Question there and then, and choose to die
and understand — and leave my body to be found in the
morning — I guess grieving everybody — couldn't bear to
leave Peter and my father so alone — afraid to die yet then
and so never took the Chance, (if there was a Chance, perhaps
somehow there was) — also as if everybody in session in
central radiotelepathic contact with the same problem — the
Great Being within ourselves — Coming back from vomit
saw a man knees to chest I thought I saw as X ray his skull
I realized he was crouched there as in shroud (with towel
mosquito protection wrapped round his face) suffering the
same trial and separation — Thought of people, saw their
images clearly, you — mysterious apparently know more than
I do now and why don't you communicate, or can't you, or
have I ignored it? — Simon seemingly an angel in his anni-
hilation of vanity and giving forth new life in children — ' If
any interplanetary news comes through ' he said ' I'll be
the first to be relaying it over the wires in a way that won't
get it fucked up ' — Francine his wife — sort of a Seraph
of Woman, all women (as all men) the same — spectral
creatures put here mysteriously to live, be the living Gods, and
suffer Crucifixion of death like Christ, but either get lost
and die in soul or get in Contact and give new birth to
continue the Process of Being (tho' they themselves die, or do
they?) — and I lost and poor Peter who depends on me for
some Heaven I haven't got, lost — and I keep rejecting
women, who come to minister to me — decided to have
children somehow, a revolution in the Hallucination — but
the suffering was about as much as I could bear and the

thought of more suffering even deeper to come made me despair — felt, still feel, like lost soul, surrounded by ministering angels (Ramon, the Maestro, yourself, the whole Common World of Diers) — and my poor mother died in God knows what state of suffering — I can't stand it — vomited again (Ramon had come over and told me to vomit off the porch where I was lying, if I had to later, very careful kind situation) I mean, is this a good group — I remember your saying watch out *whose* vision you get — but God knows I don't know who to turn to finally when the Chips are down spiritually and I have to depend on my own Serpent-self's memory of Merry Visions of Blake — or depend on nothing and enter anew — but enter what? — Death? — and at that moment — vomiting still feeling like a Great lost Serpent-seraph vomiting in consciousness of the Transfiguration to come — with the Radiotelepathy sense of a Being whose presence I had not yet fully sensed — too Horrible for me, still — to accept the fact of total communication with say everyone an eternal seraph male and female at once — and me a lost soul seeking help — well slowly the intensity began to fade, I being incapable of moving in any direction spiritually — not knowing who to look to or what to look for — not quite trusting to ask the Maestro — tho' in the vision of the scene it was he who was the local logical Ministering Spirit to trust, if anyone — went over and sat by him (as Ramon gently suggested) to be ' blown ' — that is he croons a song to you to cure your soul and blows smoke at you — rather a comforting presence — tho' by now the steep fear had passed — that being over got up and took my piece of cloth I brought against mosquitos and went home in moonlight with plump Ramon — who said the more you saturate yourself with Ayahuasca the deeper you go — visit the moon, see the dead, see God — see Tree Spirits — etc.

I hardly have the nerve to go back, afraid of some real madness, a Changed Universe permanently changed — tho' I guess change it must for me someday — much less as planned before, go up the river six hours to drink with an Indian tribe — I suppose I will — meanwhile will wait here another week in Pucallpa and drink a few more times with same group — I wish I knew who, if anyone, there is to work with that *knows,* if anyone knows, who I am or what I am. I wish I could hear from you. I think I'll be here long enough for a letter to reach me — write

Allen Ginsberg

If I do leave here before 2 weeks and letter arrives it will be forwarded to me promptly in Lima so I'll hear from you there but I do want to hear from you Bill so please write and advise me whatever you can if you can. I don't know if I'm going mad or not and it's difficult to face more — tho' I suppose I will be able to protect myself by treating *that* consciousness as a temporary illusion and return to temporary normal consciousness when the effects wear off — (I began to glimpse the Call of Haitian Voodoo) — but this almost schizophrenic alteration of consciousness is fearful — and also the sense of not knowing who, personally, around me to open up to. I had arrangements to bring some back to NY but am almost afraid to — I'm no Curandero, I'm lost myself, and afraid of giving a nightmare I can't stop to others like Peter.

I don't know how all this sounds to you but you know me reasonably well so write, fast, please.

Everything is OK, I suppose, in case this all just worries you unnecessarily, I'll be all right —

Love,   Allen

P.S. The last hours, in bookstore this morning buying this
pen heard old nostalgic Nelson Eddy record of ' Maytime '
I used to play over in childhood and it was like a reminder
of Death, so sad — ' will you love me ever? '
Extra added Attraction — some excerpts from Ether notes
I took 2 weeks ago in Lima, in a minor key.

> The ringing sound in all the senses
> > of everything that has ever been Created
> > all the combinations recurring over and
> > > over again as before —

> Every possible Combination of Being — all
> > the old ones :— all the old Hindu.
> Sabahadabadie-pluralic universes
> ringing in Grandiloquent
> > > Bearded Juxtaposition
> with all their minarets and moonlit
> > > towers enlaced with iron
> > > > or porcelain embroidery,
> all have existed —
> > > and the Sages with
> white hair who sat crosslegged on
> > > a female couch —
> hearkening to whatever music came
> > > from out the wood or street,
> whatever bird that whistled in the marketplace
> whatever note the clock struck to say
> > > Time —
> whatever drug, or aire, they breathed
> > to make them think so deep
> > > or hear so simply what
> > > had passed
> like a car passing in the 1960 street

beside the Governmental Palace
in Peru, this Lima,
in the year I write —

A Buddha as of old, with the sirens of
whatever machinery making ringing noises in
the street.
And streetlight reflected in the RR station
front facade window in a
dinky port in Backwash
of the murky forgotton
fabulous whatever
Civilisation of
Eternity :—
with the RR station clock ring midnight,
as of now,
and waiting for the 6th,
to write a word,
and end on the last chime — remember
this *one* twelve was struck
before
and never again; both.

and I turn back from the balcony where I stood
looking at the Cross (afraid)
and stars
thinking of the BONG of midnight —
Sages of Asia, or the white beards in Persia,
Scribbling on the margins of their scrolls
in delicate ink
remembering with tears the ancient clockbells of their
cities
and the cities that had been — and

Affirm with laughing eyes —
the world is as we see it,
    male and female, passing
as it passes through the years,
        as has before and will, perhaps
    with all its countless pearls
And all the bloody noses of Eternity —
                    and all the old mistakes —
                        including
this old consciousness, which has seen
itself before — (thus the locust-whistle
of antiquity's nightwatch in my eardrum)

                    I'm scribbling
nothings,
page upon page of profoundest
                nothing,
as scribed the Ancient Hebe, when
            he wrote Adonoi or One —
all to amuse or make money or deceive —

> **O BELL TIME, RING THY
> MIDNIGHT FOR THE BILLIONTH
> SOUNDY TIME, I HEAR AGAIN!**

June 21   1960   Present Time   Pre-Sent Time
Cargo American Express
London   England

Dear Allen :

There is no thing to fear. Vaya adelante. Look. Listen.
Hear. Your AYUASKA consciousness is more valid than
'Normal Consciousness'? Whose 'Normal Consciousness'?
Why return to? Why are you surprised to see me? You are
following in my steps. I know thee way. And yes know the
area better than you I think. Tried more than once to tell you
to communicate what I know. You did not or could not
listen. 'You can not show to anyone what he has not seen.'
Brion Gysin* for Hassan Sabbah. Listen now? Take the
enclosed copy of this letter. Cut along the lines. Rearrange
putting section one by section three and section two by section
four. Now read aloud and you will hear My Voice. Whose
voice? Listen. Cut and rearrange in any combination. Read
aloud. I can not choose but hear. Dont think about it. Dont
theorize. Try it. Do the same with your poems. With any
poems any prose. Try it. You want 'Help'. Here it is. Pick it
up on it. And always remember. 'Nothing is True. Everything
is permitted.' Last Words of Hassan Sabbah The Old Man
Of The Mountain.

---

* Brion Gysin : an English painter, collaborator and friend of Burroughs from Tanger, who suggested to him the application of
XX Century painter's techniques — the collage — to written composition. *Naked Lunch* was thus finished as a collage of routines. The
pamphlets *Minutes to Go* (Two Cities Press, Paris 1960) and *The
Exterminator* (Auerhahn Press, San Francisco 1960) were prepared
by Gysin, Burroughs, Gregory Corso and others as graphic exposition
of an immediate way out of temporal literary and phenomenological
hang-ups through collage cut-up techniques. — A.G.

LISTEN TO MY LAST WORDS ANY WORLD. LISTEN
ALL YOU BOARDS SYNDICATES AND GOVERN-
MENTS OF THE EARTH. AND YOU POWER POWERS
BEHIND WHAT FILTH DEALS CONSUMMATED IN
WHAT LAVATORY TO TAKE WHAT IS NOT YOURS.
TO SELL THE GROUND FROM UNBORN FEET.
LISTEN. WHAT I HAVE TO SAY IS FOR ALL MEN
EVERYWHERE. I REPEAT FOR ALL. NO ONE IS
EXCLUDED. FREE TO ALL WHO PAY. FREE TO ALL
WHO PAIN PAY.

WHAT SCARED YOU ALL INTO TIME? WHAT
SCARED YOU ALL INTO YOUR BODIES? INTO SHIT
FOREVER? DO YOU WANT TO STAY THERE FOR-
EVER? THEN LISTEN TO THE LAST WORDS OF
HASSAN SABBAH. LISTEN LOOK OR SHIT FOREVER.
LISTEN LOOK OR SHIT FOREVER. WHAT SCARED
YOU INTO TIME? INTO BODY? INTO SHIT? I WILL
TELL YOU. THE WORD. THE-THEE WORD. IN THEE
BEGINNING WAS THE WORD. SCARED YOU ALL
INTO SHIT FOREVER. COME OUT FOREVER. COME
OUT OF THE TIME WORD THE FOREVER. COME
OUT OF THE BODY WORD THEE FOREVER. COME
OUT OF THE SHIT WORD THE FOREVER. ALL OUT
OF TIME AND INTO SPACE. FOREVER. THERE IS
NO THING TO FEAR. THERE IS NO THING IN
SPACE. THAT IS ALL ALL ALL HASSAN SABBAH.
THERE IS NO WORD TO FEAR. THERE IS NO WORD.
THAT IS ALL ALL ALL HASSAN SABBAH. IF YOU I
CANCEL ALL YOUR WORDS FOREVER. AND THE
WORDS OF HASSAN SABBAH I AS ALSO CANCEL.
ACROSS ALL YOUR SKIES SEE THE SILENT WRIT-
ING OF BRION GYSIN HASSAN SABBAH. THE WRIT-
ING OF SPACE. THE WRITING OF SILENCE.

LOOK   LOOK   LOOK

AMIGOS MUCHACHOS A TRAVES DE TODOS SUS
CIELOS VEA LA ESCRITURA SILENCIOSA DE BRION
GYSIN HASSAN SABBAH. LA ESCRITURA DE SILEN-
CIO LA ESCRITURA DE ESPACIO. ESO ES TODO
TODO TODO HASSAN SABBAH.

VEA   VEA   VEA

When will you return — ? The Cut Up Method is explained
in *Minutes to Go*. Which is already out in the States. I will
send you a copy but where to? George Whitman says to look
up his old friend Silvester de Castro in Panama City. Connected with the municipal symphony and the University.
Hasta Al Vista Amigo.

> Best
>
> William Burroughs
> For Hassan Sabbah
> *Fore! Hassan Sabbah*

PS. NO ONE IN HIS SENSES WOULD TRUST 'THE
UNIVERSE'. SWEPT WITH CON THE MILLIONS
STOOD UNDER THE SIGNS. WHO EVER PAID OFF
A MARK A GOOK AN APE A HUMAN ANIMAL? NO
BODY EXCEPT HASSAN SABBAH

EPILOGUE (1963)

San Francisco
August 28, 1963

To whom it may concern :

Self deciphers this correspondence thus : the vision of ministering angels my fellow man and woman first wholly glimpsed while the Curandero gently crooned human in Ayahuasca trance-state 1960 was prophetic of transfiguration of self consciousness from homeless mind sensation of eternal fright to incarnate body feeling present bliss now actualized 1963.

Old love, as ever
Allen Ginsberg

I AM DYING, MEESTER ?

Panama clung to our bodies — Probably cut — Anything made this dream — It has consumed the customers of fossil orgasm — Ran into my old friend Jones — So badly off, forgotten, coughing in 1920 movie — Vaudeville voices hustle sick dawn breath on bed service — Idiot Mambo spattered backwards — I nearly suffocated trying on the boy's breath — That's Panama — Nitrous flesh swept out by your voice and end of receiving set — Brain eating birds patrol the low frequency brain waves — Post card waiting forgotten civilians 'and they are all on jelly fish, Meester — Panama photo town — Dead post card of junk.'

Sad hand down backward time track — Genital pawn ticket peeled his stale underwear — Brief boy on screen laughing my skivies all the way down — Whispers of dark street in Puerto Assis — Meester smiles through the village wastrel — Orgasm siphoned back telegram : ' Johnny pants down '. — (That stale summer dawn smell in the garage — Vines twisting through steel — Bare feet in dog's excrement.)

Panama clung to our bodies from Las Palmas to David on camphor sweet smells of cooking paregoric — Burned down the republic — The druggist no glot clom Fliday — Panama mirrors of 1910 under seal in any drug store — He threw in the towel, morning light on cold coffee —

Junk kept nagging me : ' Lushed in East St. Louis, I *knew* you'd come scraping bone — Once a junky always spongy and rotten — I *knew* your life — Junk sick four days there.'

Stale breakfast table — Little cat smile — Pain and death smell of his sickness in the room with me — Three souvenir shots of Panama city — Old friend came and stayed all day — Face eaten by ' I need *more* ' — I have noticed this in the New World — ' You come with me, Meester? '

And Joselito moved in at Las Playas during the essentials — Stuck in this place — Iridescent lagoons, swamp delta, gas flares — Bubbles of coal gas still be saying ' A ver, Luckees! ' a hundred years from now — A rotting teak wood balcony propped up by Ecuador.

' The brujo began crooning a special case — It was like going under ether into the eyes of a shrunken head — Numb, covered with layers of cotton — Don't know if you got my last hints trying to break out of this numb dizziness with Chinese characters — All I want is out of here — Hurry up please — Took possession of me — How many plots have made a botanical expedition like this before they could take place? — Scenic railways — I am dying cross wine dizziness — I was saying over and over " shifted commissions where the awning flaps " Flashes in front of my eyes your voice and end of the line.'

That whinning Panama clung to our bodies — I went into Chico's Bar on mouldy pawn ticket, waiting in 1920 movie for a rum coke — Nitrous flesh under this honky tonk swept out by your voice : ' Driving Nails In My Coffin ' — Brain eating birds patrol ' Your Cheating Heart ' — Dead post card waiting a place forgotten — Light concussion of 1920 movie — Casual adolescent had undergone special G.I. processing — Evening on the boy's flesh naked — Kept trying to touch in sleep — ' Old photographer trick wait for Johnny — Here goes Mexican cemetery.' On the sea wall met a boy with red and white striped T shirt — P. G. town in the purple twilight — The boy pealed off his stale underwear scraping erection — Warm rain on the iron roof — Under the ceiling fan stood naked on bed service — Bodies touched electric film, contact sparks tingled — Fan whiffs of young hard on washing adolescent T shirt — The blood smells drowned voices and end of the line — That's Panama — Sad movie drifting in islands of rubbish, black lagoons and fish people waiting a place forgotten — Fossil honky tonk swept out by a ceiling fan — Old photographer trick tuned them out.

' I am dying, Meester? '

Flashes in front of my eyes naked and sullen — Rotten dawn wind in sleep — Death rot on Panama photo where the awning flaps.

William Burroughs